Clem Goes to Sch

by Jennica Sterling
illustrated by Carol Nicklaus

What will Glen do today?

2

Glen will go to school.
He will not be late.

What will Clem do today?

4

Clem will not go away.
She will play here.

What will Glen do today?

What will Glen do today?

Glen will go to school.
He will not be late.

What will Clem do today?
Clem will not go away.

Why?
Clem will have school here!

Comprehension Check

Retell the Story

Use a Sequence Chart to retell the story in order.

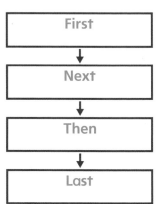

Think and Compare

1. What happens on Tuesday?

2. Why is it fun to play school with your friends?

3. Why do little children look forward to their first day of school?

16